This bite-sized boo̶̶k̶̶...
useful overvie̶w̶...
and help you to̶...

- Understand ̶...
- Prioritise you̶...̶...̶.̶...g.
- Safeguard you̶...
- Discover ways ̶...̶...en off and relax.
- Boost your energy levels and feel alert.
- Manage stress and avoid burnout.

It's up to you today to start
making healthy choices.
Not choices that are just healthy
for your body, but healthy
for your mind

Steve Maraboli

Why is self-care so important?

The World Health Organisation defines health as "a state of complete physical, mental and social wellbeing and not merely the absence of disease or infirmity". Self-care and wellbeing are strongly linked to happiness and life satisfaction. In short, self-care and wellbeing can be described as how you feel about yourself and your life.

The act of making your own personal wellbeing your number one priority has nothing to do with being selfish. No one needs to feel guilty or ashamed about this. It is the most responsible way to live your life and you have a duty to look after yourself and invest in self-care.

Happiness is not a matter
of intensity but of balance,
order, rhythm and harmony

Thomas Merton

Life balance

We are living in a volatile, uncertain and complex world. Life seems to be so much about rushing around and trying to keep lots of balls in the air. It is so important to bear in mind that for all the time you are on output, you need to balance this with rest and relaxation so that you can recover and recharge.

Too much work and not enough time out for yourself can result in physical and mental health problems. Being disciplined about setting time aside for yourself is essential in achieving better balance and living a happier and healthier life.

The seven wisdoms of wellbeing

© Liggy Webb

- Spiritual wellbeing
- Emotional wellbeing
- Physical wellbeing
- Social wellbeing
- Financial wellbeing
- Digital wellbeing
- Environmental wellbeing

The holistic approach to wellbeing

There are many components to wellbeing and the real wisdom is the consideration and practical application of each of the following:

Emotional wellbeing - constructively channelling emotions to maintain positive mental health

Physical wellbeing - combining healthy eating, exercise, relaxation and sleep to manage energy and stress levels and support immunity

Social wellbeing - feeling included and connected

Financial wellbeing - being able to make informed choices to enjoy life, both now and in retirement

Digital wellbeing - managing the influences and impact of technologies and digital services

Environmental wellbeing - occupying a healthy, enjoyable and stimulating environment

Spiritual wellbeing - finding meaning and purpose

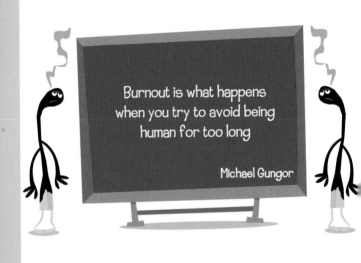

Burnout is what happens
when you try to avoid being
human for too long

Michael Gungor

Self-care and burnout

Burnout is a state of emotional, physical and mental exhaustion caused by excessive and prolonged stress. It occurs when an individual feels overwhelmed, emotionally drained, and unable to meet constant demands.

For a multitude of reasons, the pace of modern life has accelerated. In a rapidly evolving world of too much choice and overwhelm, it can be challenging to establish a healthy balance. Everyday pressures can build up and affect our stress levels without us even being aware that it is happening. The creep of burnout can be insidious, and cultivating healthy habits through a self-care strategy is the best way to avoid it. The following pages will offer plenty of good advice and easy tips to help you take the best care of yourself.

How to look after yourself

Find time for yourself

Making your own personal wellbeing a priority and creating some "me time" is essential for self-care. If you spend your life running around after everyone else, to the detriment of your own wellbeing, eventually you will burn out and those people will then need to look after you!

When you create your daily to-do list, make sure you put yourself on it and carve out some valuable "me time". You are definitely worth it!

To be kind to others you must first be kind to yourself

Unknown

Be kind to yourself

Valuing and treating yourself with the same kindness and respect that you would give your best friend is so important. Giving yourself a hard time and being self-critical about every imperfection and every mistake you make is not helpful.

You were not born to be perfect, you were born to be real, and real people mess up from time to time – and that is perfectly OK. Liking, respecting and looking after yourself is very important in terms of your emotional wellbeing.

You are not required to set yourself on fire to keep other people warm

Unknown

Set healthy boundaries

You may well have an inner superhero who likes to think they are super-capable. It is really important when it comes to self-care to be realistic of your own capacity. You simply cannot be everything to everybody. Personal boundaries are an important part of managing unnecessary stress and avoiding overload.

Having healthy boundaries is about knowing and understanding your limits. To set healthy boundaries you need to consider what you can tolerate and accept, and what makes you feel uncomfortable or stressed. Boundaries are a sign of a healthy and respectful relationship with yourself, so be disciplined about preserving them.

Take a rest; a field that has rested gives a bountiful crop

Ovid

Slow down

Taking time to just slow down, relax and rest is one of the best ways that you can recharge. It is also one of the best ways to ensure that you are pacing yourself and ensuring a healthy balance. Focusing on the moment and appreciating the experience, rather than being somewhere else, will heighten your enjoyment of whatever activity you are involved in.

Focusing on all your senses will help you to appreciate much more of what is going on around you, which in turn can have a very relaxing effect. Being around nature and green spaces can also be energising and lift your mood, which will ultimately help you to be more productive.

19

Practice mindfulness

The term "mindfulness" comes from Eastern spiritual and religious traditions. It is a very old concept and is a key part of Buddhism and also appears in Hindu writings. A great deal of scientific research now shows that the mindful approach to stress, anxiety and mental health is a very helpful and popular way of dealing with and diffusing high levels of stress.

Mindfulness refers to being completely in touch with and aware of the present moment, as well as taking a non-evaluative and non-judgmental approach to your inner experience. It is essentially about being present and noticing what is around you. So often, if you are not careful, you can find yourself racing through life in a mad dash and not taking time to stop and really appreciate what is going on around you. Discover the power of a pause.

Sometimes the most productive
thing you can do is relax

Mark Black

Key benefits of relaxation

- Lowers your blood pressure.
- Slows your breathing rate.
- Slows your heart rate.
- Reduces activity of stress hormones.
- Increases blood flow to major muscles.
- Reduces muscle tension and chronic pain.
- Improves concentration and mood.
- Maintains normal blood sugar levels.
- Improves your digestion.
- Boosts your energy levels.
- Supports your mental health.
- Helps you to be present and appreciate the moment.

I want someone who will look
at me the same way I look
at chocolate cake

Anonymous

Healthy eating

No matter who you are or where you live, the very fact that you are alive depends on you eating and keeping hydrated. A delicious meal and a drink can be one of the most satisfying sensory experiences and can also be responsible for some of our greatest health problems.

You are essentially what you eat. Each human being is made up of water, protein, fat, minerals and vitamins. Every single molecule comes from the food you eat and the water you drink. Eating the highest quality food in the right quantities helps you to achieve your highest potential for health, vitality and freedom from disease.

Strengthen your immune system

Following good-health guidelines is the best way to keep your immune system strong and healthy. Get started by building these 10 healthy habits into your everyday life.

1. Wash your hands frequently.
2. Eat a healthy balanced diet.
3. Exercise and relax regularly.
4. Maintain a healthy weight.
5. Reduce refined sugar.
6. Don't smoke.
7. Moderate alcohol consumption.
8. Make sure you get adequate sleep.
9. Manage and reduce stress levels.
10. Think positively and be kind.

Exercise

Exercise is vital for maintaining mental fitness, and it can reduce stress. Studies show that it is very effective at reducing fatigue, improving alertness and concentration, and enhancing overall cognitive function. When stress affects the brain, with its many nerve connections, the rest of the body feels the impact as well. So it stands to reason that if your body feels better, so does your mind.

Being active doesn't necessarily mean a trip to the gym, just getting outside in the fresh air for a brisk walk can be very beneficial! Devices to measure how many steps you walk a day can also be very motivating. Setting yourself a target to walk 10,000 steps a day is recommended for a healthy heart, as well as having positive effects on your mental health.

Lighten your load

Take a good look at your life and work out what is really important. It can be so easy to accumulate stuff and overcomplicate your life if you are not careful. This will not help you to feel relaxed. There is real beauty in keeping things as simple as possible and avoiding "stuffocation"!

Decluttering and being tidy both at work and home will help you to feel far more organised and calm. It can be stressful trying to find things in a cluttered environment. Every now and then it can be very therapeutic and cleansing to have a sort out and decide what you don't really need any more.

Get creative

Having more opportunities to express your creativity will help you to keep enthusiastic and motivated about possibilities. Creative people also tend to be more optimistic and resilient. A recent study in the *Journal of Positive Psychology* indicated that engaging in a creative activity just once a day can lead to a more positive state of mind.

Switch off

It is becoming increasingly obvious that our world is developing an unhealthy attachment to technology and mobile devices. Being able to switch off from technology will help you to relax quite significantly.

Various studies into neurological and emotional wellbeing highlight the need to take breaks. Scanning social media is not a break for your brain because your mind will think it is still working. When you relax, you really need to switch off and avoid directing your thoughts toward any task at all. Downtime is healthy for the mind, body and soul.

Balance your intake of information

For the sake of your mental health it is worth bearing in mind that there is a great deal of information in circulation – some of it is very valuable and important, some of it is fake and toxic. This can have a detrimental impact on your wellbeing. Don't believe every story you read, and always fact-check against a reliable and well-evidenced source.

It is also important to balance your intake of daily news and for every negative thing you hear or read, make sure that you actively seek out some positive stories that will uplift you. A healthy balance is essential for your mental health and wellbeing.

Think positively

Thinking positively is not about putting your head in the sand and being unrealistic, as some people may believe. With a positive attitude you can also recognise the negative aspects of a situation and make a conscious decision to focus instead on the hope and opportunity that is available.

Thinking positively will release you from getting locked in a paralysing loop of negative emotion and allows you to bounce back from adversity and challenging experiences.

Manage your mind chatter

We literally have tens of thousands of thoughts a day and the quality of those thoughts will have a big impact on how relaxed you feel. Negative mind chatter can be exhausting, especially if you are worried about something and it is playing on your mind. Reframing your thoughts can be really helpful in calming negative thinking.

Here are five questions to help you reframe your negative thoughts:

1. What else could this mean?
2. Am I jumping to negative conclusions?
3. What is the best part about this situation or person?
4. Am I filtering out the positives and dwelling on the negatives?
5. What are the benefits of these thoughts to me?

Avoid energy drains

Some people can behave like doom goblins and actively try to bring other people down and suck the joy out of situations. They do this by constantly seeking out the negative and this can be draining on your energy and wellbeing.

Social media in some cases can be a playground for toxic behaviour and a place where gossip-mongering is rife. Even just reading some of the unnecessarily hurtful comments about other people fuels the bandwagon and can contaminate your own thinking. Be aware of people and situations that drain your energy and focus on something more uplifting.

Reach out and connect

Building and sustaining a strong network of supportive friends, family and work colleagues can really help during times of difficulty. It is important to have people in your life who you can trust and confide in. While simply talking about a situation with a friend or loved one will not necessarily make troubles go away, it will allow you to share your feelings, gain support and explore possible solutions to your problems.

Listening to other people's experiences can be really useful and, although you can't always learn from others' mistakes, there is bound to be some good advice out there.

Let the laughter in

Having a good laugh can decrease stress hormones and also increase immune cells and infection-fighting antibodies. Laughter has so many benefits and can be such a great tonic, as well as helping you to relax. Even in challenging times it helps to seek out the funny side of situations.

Laughter also triggers the release of endorphins, the body's natural feel-good chemicals. Endorphins promote an overall sense of wellbeing and can even temporarily relieve pain, as well as having a very positive effect on your emotional wellbeing.

Take a daily dose of vitamin G

Vitamin G is vitamin gratitude. Grateful people report higher levels of positive emotions, life satisfaction, vitality and optimism, and lower levels of depression and stress. Cultivating an attitude of gratitude can enhance the feel-good factor.

Each day you are gifted 86,400 seconds. How many do you use to say thank you? Taking time out each day to stop and focus on the things you are grateful for can help you to establish moments of calm and happiness. There are many ways to practice gratitude. Keeping a daily journal, identifying and sharing the highlights of your day and simply making a point of being more appreciative can help you to absorb your daily dose of vitamin gratitude.

Sleep is the golden chain that
ties health and our bodies together

Thomas Dekker

Sleep

Sleep can so often be an overlooked and neglected component of overall health and wellbeing. It is so important because it enables your body to repair and be fit for the day ahead. Various studies suggest that getting adequate sleep may also help prevent excess weight gain, heart disease and increased illness during times of stress.

If you are challenged with sleepless nights you will know how it feels to have your mind buzzing with anxiety while you are desperately tossing and turning with frustration. Relaxation can help you switch off and promote much better quality of sleep which, in turn, will help you to recharge your batteries and cope better generally.

Be kind

The ability to experience and integrate meaning and purpose in your life is an important way to boost your wellbeing. This may be through your own faith or through social connectivity, art, music, literature or nature. There is one way that we can all incorporate meaning and purpose into our lives and that is through kindness.

Wherever possible (and it is always possible), be kind. Every day of your life there will be ways you can practice kindness. So go out there and discover what they are. Life is a precious gift and every living human being has the opportunity to make a positive difference.

Building a culture of kindness

Rules of being human

(Handed down from ancient Sanskrit)

1. You will receive a body
2. You will learn lessons
3. There are no mistakes, only lessons
4. A lesson will be repeated until it is learned
5. Learning lessons does not end
6. 'There' is no better than 'here'
7. Others are merely mirrors of you
8. What you make of your life is up to you
9. Life is exactly what you think it is
10. Your answers lie inside you
11. You will forget all of this
12. You can remember it whenever you want

Useful websites

If you are looking for more in-depth advice and don't know where to go, these websites have been helpful in researching this book. They have been curated for the excellent work they do in providing information about self-care.

- thriveglobal.com
- calm.com
- oxfordmindfulness.org
- headspace.com
- buddhify.com
- mind.org.uk
- actionforhappiness.org
- who.int
- nhs.uk/live-well/eat-well
- together-uk.org